Literature & Comprehension

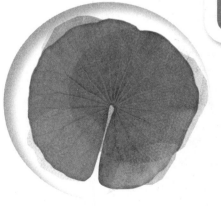

Language Arts

Activity Book

K12®

Book Staff and Contributors

Kristen Kinney-Haines *Director, Primary Literacy*
Alane Gernon-Paulsen *Content Specialist*
Anna Day *Senior Instructional Designer*
Cheryl Howard, Lenna King *Instructional Designers*
Mary Beck Desmond *Senior Text Editor*
Karen Ingebretsen, Allyson Jacob *Text Editors*
Suzanne Montazer *Creative Director, Print and ePublishing*
Jayoung Cho *Senior Print Visual Designer*
Jacquie Rosenborough *Print Visual Designer*
Stephanie Shaw Williams *Cover Designer*
Kandee Dyczko, Tisha Ruibal *Writers*
Amy Eward *Senior Manager, Writers*
Susan Raley *Senior Manager, Editors*
Deanna Lacek *Project Manager*
David Johnson *Director, Program Management Grades K–8*

Maria Szalay *Executive Vice President, Product Development*
John Holdren *Senior Vice President, Content and Curriculum*
David Pelizzari *Vice President, K^{12} Content*
Kim Barcas *Vice President, Creative*
Laura Seuschek *Vice President, Assessment and Research*
Aaron Hall *Vice President, Program Management*

Lisa Dimaio Iekel *Senior Production Manager*
Ray Traugott *Production Manager*

Credits

All illustrations © K12 unless otherwise noted
Waterlily, leungchopan/Shutterstock.com; lily leaf © Videowokart/Dreamstime.com;
orange koi © Eric IsselTe/Fotolia.com

About K12 Inc.

K12 Inc., a technology-based education company, is the nation's leading provider of proprietary curriculum and online education programs to students in grades K–12. K^{12} provides its curriculum and academic services to online schools, traditional classrooms, blended school programs, and directly to families. K12 Inc. also operates the K^{12} International Academy, an accredited, diploma-granting online private school serving students worldwide. K^{12}'s mission is to provide any child the curriculum and tools to maximize success in life, regardless of geographic, financial, or demographic circumstances. K12 Inc. is accredited by CITA. More information can be found at www.K12.com.

978-1-60153-208-4
Printed by R.R. Donnelley, Kendallville, IN, USA, May 2016

Contents

Literature & Comprehension

Our Place in Space

If You're Happy and You Know It

Semester Review and Checkpoint

Literature & Comprehension

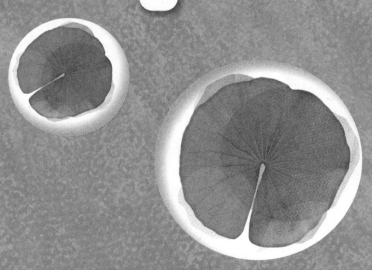

Explore *Bedtime for Frances*

Bedtime Buddies

Draw a picture of yourself in bed with something that helps you fall asleep. Then, complete the sentence.

My _____
helps me fall asleep.

Explore Poems About Games
A Swing with a View

Draw a picture of what you see when you go high in the air on a swing. Then, complete the sentence.

When I swing, I can see _____

_____.

Explore "Sing a Song of People"
A People Picture

Draw a picture of one of the ways
people move around a city.
Then, complete the sentence.

My picture shows how people _____

_____ .

LITERATURE & COMPREHENSION

Explore Poems About Animals (A)
Don't You Know It, I'm a Poet

Circle the rhyming words in "A Poem." Then, fill in the blanks to write your own poem.

A Poem

by Anonymous

I like my shiny hat.
I like my yellow shoe.
I like the spotted cat
I visit at the zoo.

A Poem

by _____

I like my shiny _____.

I like my yellow _____.

I like the spotted _____.

I visit at the _____.

Explore *The Legend of the Bluebonnet*
Character Map

Fill in the character map.

	The Legend of the Bluebonnet	"The Legend of the Dipper"
Main character's name		
Family in story		
What does she do to help others?		
What words describe her?		

LITERATURE & COMPREHENSION

Explore "Medio Pollito: The Little Half-Chick"
Compare and Contrast Characters

Fill in the chart to compare and contrast characters from "Medio Pollito: The Little Half-Chick" and "The Legend of the Dipper."

	Words that describe	Meets others on the road?	Helps others?	Good or bad ending for character?
Medio Pollito				
Girl in "The Legend of the Dipper"				

Explore "Wynken, Blynken, and Nod"
Imagine Sailing Away

Draw a picture of what you imagine in your head when you hear the poem. Then, complete the sentence.

When I hear "Wynken, Blynken, and Nod," I imagine

_____ .

Explore "The Owl and the Pussycat"
Follow the Owl and the Pussycat

1. Cut out the pictures.
2. Put the pictures in the order that they happen in the poem.
3. Glue the pictures in order.

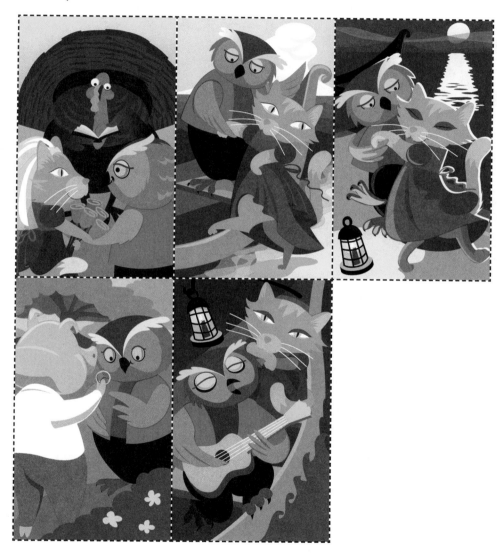

LITERATURE & COMPREHENSION

Glue the pictures in the order that they happen in "The Owl and the Pussycat."

Explore "King Midas"
The Golden Touch

Draw a picture of something you love. Use glitter to turn it to gold. Then, complete the sentence.

I would turn my _____ into gold because

_____.

Explore Poems About the Weather (A)
Who Am I?

Read a riddle, and then fill in the blank to answer the question.

Riddle 1

I'm big and blue all through the day,
But I turn black when the sun is away.

Who am I? _____

Riddle 2

I'm long and orange.
I have no feet.
I grow underground.
I'm a crunchy treat!

Who am I? _____

LITERATURE & COMPREHENSION

Introduce "Strong Wind's Bride"
Retell "Strong Wind's Bride"

1. Cut out the pictures.
2. Glue the pictures in order.
3. Retell "Strong Wind's Bride" using the pictures.

LITERATURE & COMPREHENSION

Glue the pictures in the order that they happen in "Strong Wind's Bride." Retell the story.

Beginning

Middle

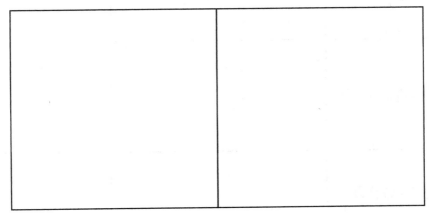

End

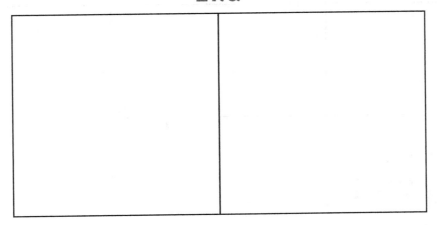

Explore "Strong Wind's Bride"
Compare Three Sisters

Fill in the chart to compare the characters in the story.

	Two older sisters	Youngest sister
How they look		
How they act		
Visit Strong Wind's sister?		
Honest?		
Can see Strong Wind?		

Explore Poems About the Weather (B)
Write a Rain Poem

Fill in the blanks to write a poem about the rain. Use words from the box to make rhymes.

Word Bank

bats	rats	cats	mats	hats
knees	peas	fleas	bees	trees

Rain, Rain

by _____

Rain on _____ .

Rain on _____ .

Rain on _____ .

Rain on _____ .

Rain on everything, especially me!

Introduce "Shedding Light on Rainbows"
What Did I Learn?

Complete the KWL chart.

Know What do we **k**now?	**Want** What do we **w**ant to find out?	**Learn** What did we **l**earn?
Rainbows happen when it rains.	What is a rainbow made of?	Sunlight is called white light.

Explore "The Woodpecker, Turtle, and Deer"
Retell the Story Using Puppets

Cut out each character, and glue it to a craft stick. Use the puppets to retell the story.

Introduce "Stone Soup"
Make Inferences from Pictures

Circle the statements that you can infer from the picture.
Cross out the ones that you can't.

Sue likes to build sand castles.	Sue is enjoying herself.	It is a cold day.
Sue likes the color yellow.	Sue is at the park.	It is a warm day.

LITERATURE & COMPREHENSION

Explore "Stone Soup"
Let's Make Some Stone Soup

Cut out the pictures, and use them to retell "Stone Soup."
Drop them in the pot in the same order as in the story.

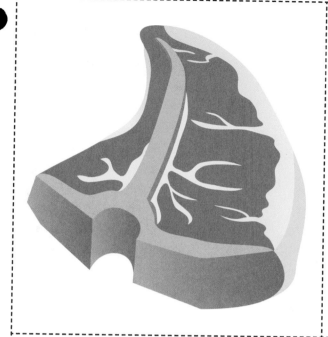

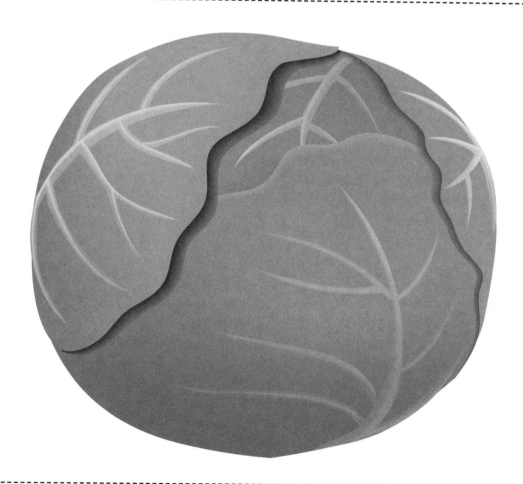

Explore "Budulinek"

Sequence Events in "Budulinek"

Cut out the pictures, and put them in order.

LITERATURE & COMPREHENSION

Glue the pictures in the order that they happen in "Budulinek." Retell the story.

Beginning

Middle

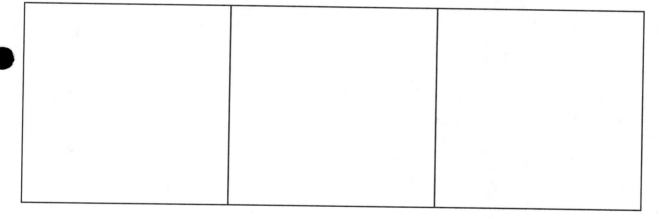

End

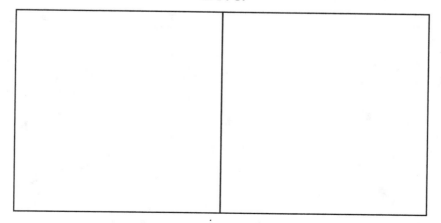

Explore "Issun Boshi"
Retell "Issun Boshi" with a Finger Puppet

Cut out the finger puppet. Use it to retell "Issun Boshi."

Introduce "The Poor Man's Reward"
Book Walk with Question Words

Fill in the blanks with questions about the "The Poor Man's Reward."

1. Who _____

   _____

   _____?

2. What _____

   _____

   _____?

3. Where _____

   _____

   _____?

LITERATURE & COMPREHENSION

4. When _____

_____

_____?

5. Why _____

_____

_____?

6. How _____

_____

_____?

Explore "The Poor Man's Reward"

More Problem and Solution in "The Poor Man's Reward"

Draw a line from each animal to the task the animal helps the poor man complete, and then retell that part of the story.

Introduce "The Water of Life"
Book Walk with Question Words

Fill in the blanks with questions about the "The Water of Life."

1. Who _____

    _____

    _____?

2. What _____

    _____

    _____?

3. Where _____

    _____

    _____?

LITERATURE & COMPREHENSION

4. When _____

_____

_____ ?

5. Why _____

_____

_____ ?

6. How _____

_____

_____ ?

Explore "The Water of Life"

Compare the Brothers in "The Water of Life"

Fill in the chart to compare the brothers in "The Water of Life."

	Words that describe characters	How do characters treat the dwarf?	Do the characters lie to the king?	Good or bad ending for characters?
Older brothers				
Youngest brother				

LITERATURE & COMPREHENSION

Explore "The Wonderful Brocade"
Compare and Contrast "The Wonderful Brocade" and "The Water of Life"

Fill in the chart to compare and contrast two stories.

	"The Wonderful Brocade"	"The Water of Life"
Setting		
Characters		
Main character		
What are the brothers trying to do?		

	"The Wonderful Brocade"	"The Water of Life"
Who do the brothers need to help?		
Who do the brothers meet that can help them?		
Which brother finds what he is looking for?		
What happens to the brothers at the end of the story?		

Introduce "Sheep in a Jeep"
Words with Long e Spelling Patterns

Fold the page into thirds so that the section labeled ① is showing. Use an accordion, or Z, fold (see the diagram). Use this Reading Aid to read "Sheep in a Jeep" with students.

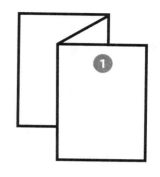

---

①

You will read "Sheep in a Jeep" with students. Stop at the points indicated and follow the instructions.

Read aloud page 13.

Ask: Did you hear any words that rhyme with *sheep? beep, jeep, steep*

STOP **Write** these words on index cards and set them aside to be sorted later in the activity.

Read aloud page 15.

Ask: Which words did you hear that rhyme with *sheep? jeep, leap*

Read aloud pages 16–19.

Ask: Did you hear any new words that rhyme with *sheep? deep*

STOP **Write** this word on an index card.

Tell students that they will hear pairs of rhyming words on the next two pages that do not rhyme with *sheep.* Have them listen carefully for the rhyming words.

Read aloud pages 20 and 21.

Ask: What pairs of rhyming words did you hear? *tug* and *shrug; yelp* and *help; out* and *shout*

Flip over to see **②**.

4

Explain that we find the long *e* sound spelled with the letters *ee* and *ea* in other words besides those that end with the letter *p*. Knowing that these spelling patterns make the long *e* sound can help us read other words.

STOP **Write** the words *team* and *seed* on index cards.

Say: Here are two more words with the long *e* sound spelled *ee* and *ea*.

Ask: Knowing that *ee* and *ea* both say /ē/, how would you read these words?

Have students read the words. If students have trouble reading these words, Touch and Say the word *team*: place your finger under the letter *t* as you say /t/, under the letters *ea* as you say /ē/, and under the letter *m* as you say /m/. Run your finger under the letters of the word as you say each sound: /t/ /ē/ /m/. Then blend the sounds together to read the word as you run your finger under the word.

Have students sound out the word *seed* in the same way.

Conclude by asking: "When you are reading and you come across a word spelled with *ee* or *ea*, what sound do those letters make?" long *e*; /ē/

3

Ask: Which words have the long *e* sound spelled with the letters *eep* as in *sheep*? *beep, jeep, steep, deep, weep, sweep*

Which words have the long *e* sound spelled with the letters *eap* as in *leap*? *heap, cheap*

How many words are spelled with the letters *eep*? 6

How many words are spelled with the letters *eap*? 2

When you read and write words with the sound /ēp/, do you think these words are more likely to be spelled with the letters *eep* or *eap*? *eep*

Can you think of any other words that were not in the story that rhyme with *sheep*? Possible answers: *keep; reap; peep; sleep*

Do you think these words are more likely to end with *–eep* or with *–eap*? *–eep*

STOP **Write** the words that students thought of on index cards, and then have students sort these words into the two groups of words from the story.

Open and fold back the page to see **4** *.*

2

Read aloud pages 23–26.

Ask: Did you hear any more words that rhyme with *sheep*? *jeep, heap, weep, sweep, cheap*

STOP **Write** any new words on index cards.

Tell students that they are now going to sort the words that rhyme with *sheep* into two groups. One group will be words spelled with the letters *eep*. The other group will be words spelled with the letters *eap*.

Place the index cards with *sheep* and *leap* as the headings for the two groups of words.

Sort the words with students. Have students read each word and place it under the heading according to how the long *e* sound is spelled. All words spelled with the ending *–eep* should be placed under the heading *sheep*. All words spelled with the ending *–eap* should be placed under the heading *leap*.

After students have sorted the words, have them read the words under each heading.

Open and fold back the page to see **3** *.*

Explore "Sheep in a Jeep"

Exclamation Marks

Cut out the sentence strips.

Jeep goes splash. ①

Jeep goes splash! ②

LITERATURE & COMPREHENSION

Explore "Sheep in a Jeep"
Exclamation Marks

Fold the page into thirds so that the section labeled **1** is showing. Use an accordion, or Z, fold (see the diagram). Use this Reading Aid to read "Sheep in a Jeep" with students.

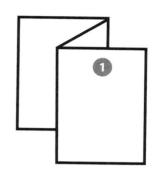

1

You will read "Sheep in a Jeep" with students. Stop at the points indicated and follow the instructions.

Read aloud page 13.

Ask: Do you see any exclamation marks on this page? Yes

Why does the story say *Beep! Beep!?* What is making the beeping noise? The sheep are honking the horn.

Say: Would a horn sound like this: Beep, beep? (*read in a normal voice*) Or would a horn sound like this: BEEP! BEEP!? (*read with expression and excitement*) BEEP! BEEP! BEEP! BEEP!

Have students reread this page with you with a lot of excitement in their voice when the text says, "Beep! Beep!"

Read aloud page 15.

Ask: Do you see any exclamation marks on this page? Yes

Should we read, "Uh-oh" in a normal voice or with excitement? with excitement

Have students reread this page with you with a lot of expression when the text says, "Uh-oh!"

Flip over to see **2**.

3

STOP **Show** students the sentence strips again.

Ask: How should we read each of these sentences? We should read the one with the period in a normal voice. We should read the one with an exclamation mark with a lot of expression and excitement.

What should we do when we're reading and we see a sentence that ends with an exclamation mark? read it with excitement

---

2

Read aloud page 18.

Point out to students that there is a lot of excitement as the jeep rolls down the hill into the mud. So the exclamations on page 18 should be read with a lot of expression.

Have students reread page 18 with you with a lot of excitement in their voice.

Read aloud page 23.

Ask: Were there any exclamations on the page we just read? Yes   Which words should we read with excitement? Oh, dear!

Have students reread page 23 with you with a lot of expression when the text says, "Oh, dear!"

STOP **Tell** students that as they read to the end of the story, you would like them to track with their finger as they read aloud, instead of you tracking the words.

Open and fold back the page to see **3**.

Explore "Sheep in a Jeep"
Act Out "Sheep in a Jeep"

Glue cotton balls onto the mask, and then cut it out.

Explore Poems About Animals (B)
Words with Short *a*

Cut out the sentence strips. Tape ① and ② together.

Fat cat ①

sat on ME ②

Explore Poems About Animals (B)
Rhyme Time

Fill in the blanks to write your own poem.

A Poem

by _____

I have a _____ .

I had a _____ .

I've got a _____ .

Inside my _____ .

Explore "Tongue-Twisters"

Build a Sentence

Cut out the sentence strips. Tape ① and ② together.

Fran fried ①

five flat fish. ②

LITERATURE & COMPREHENSION

Explore "Tongue-Twisters"
Two More Tongue Twisters

Write two tongue twisters. Then, draw a picture of one of the tongue twisters.

A big brown bear _____

_____

_____ .

_____

_____

_____ .

LITERATURE & COMPREHENSION

Introduce "Morris Has a Cold"
Quotations and Dialogue

Fold the page into thirds so that the section labeled ❶ is showing. Use an accordion, or Z, fold (see the diagram). Use this Reading Aid to read "Morris Has a Cold" with students.

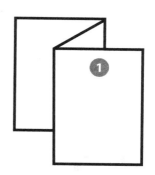

❶

You will read "Morris Has a Cold" with students. Stop at the points indicated and follow the instructions.

• • • • • • • • • • • • • • • • • • • •

Read aloud the first paragraph on page 66.

Ask: Who is speaking aloud? Morris the Moose

What does Morris say? "I have a cold. My nose is walking."

STOP **Point to the quotation marks and say:** We can tell that a character is speaking aloud when we see quotation marks. Quotation marks always come in pairs. The words inside the quotation marks are what the character says aloud.

Read aloud to the end of page 66.

Ask: Can you point to other quotation marks on this page?

There is another character talking to Morris. Who is it? Boris the Bear

What does Boris say? "You mean your nose is running." How do you know that Boris is the one who said that? The story says *Boris the Bear said.*

STOP **Point to** the word *said.*

Explain that the word *said* is another clue that a character is speaking.

Flip over to see ❷.

2

Read aloud page 68.

Ask: Are Boris and Morris speaking to each other here? Yes

How do you know that they're speaking aloud to each other? quotation marks; the word *said*

How can we tell which character is saying what? *The story says Boris said or Morris said.*

STOP On page 68, point to the opening quotation mark on line 2.

Tell students that when we see an opening quotation mark, we know that the first word a character will say is the word right after that quotation mark.

Ask: In the sentence "Boris said, 'Let me feel your forehead,'" what is the first word that Boris says? *Let*

Does Boris say the words *Boris said?* No How do you know? because there aren't quotation marks around *Boris said*; the first quotation mark is right before *Let*, so that tells us that Boris isn't talking aloud before that

Open and fold back the page to see **3**.

3

Read aloud pages 69 and 70.

STOP **At the top of page 70, point to** and read aloud the second sentence.

Ask: Is Boris telling Morris something or is he asking something? asking How can you tell? Possible answers: the question mark; the word *asked*

Tell students that the word *asked* is another clue that a character is speaking aloud. It's a clue that the character is asking a question aloud.

Tell students that when you read the next two pages, you will read the parts for Boris, and they will read the parts for Morris.

Have students track with their finger to check that they are matching their voice to the print.

Read aloud pages 71–73.

STOP **On page 72, point to** and reread the last two lines.

Ask: Which words does Boris say aloud? *stick out your tongue* How can you tell? They are inside the quotation marks.

Read aloud the rest of the story.

STOP **Ask students to point to quotation marks in the story.**

Ask: What do the quotation marks tell us? that a character is speaking aloud

What are other clues that a character is speaking aloud? the words *said* and *asked*

Explore "Morris Has a Cold"

"Morris Has a Cold"

Fold the page into thirds so that the section labeled
1 is showing. Use an accordion, or Z, fold (see the
diagram). Use this Reading Aid to read "Morris Has a
Cold" with students.

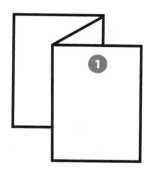

1

You will read "Morris Has a Cold" with
students. Stop at the points indicated and
follow the instructions.

Read aloud pages 66–69.

STOP **On page 69, point to** line 4.

What does Morris say? *"I have a cold. My
nose is walking."*

Ask: Do you see a word in all capital letters?
Yes How do you think we should read that
word? in a loud voice; with a raised voice

Have students reread the line of text, raising
their voice when they read the word *one*.

Read aloud page 70.

Ask: How do you think Boris says the word
inside, the last word on the page? in a loud
voice; with a raised voice

Have students reread the last two lines on the
page, raising their voice when they read the
word *inside*.

Read aloud page 71.

STOP **Point to** the words *no no no no*, which
are followed by exclamation marks.

Flip over to see **2**.

3

Read aloud the rest of the story.

STOP **Point to the last sentence of the story and ask:** How do you think Boris says this sentence? really loud

Have students reread the last sentence the way they imagine Boris would say it.

STOP **Have students to point to a word written in all capital letters.**

Ask: What do the words written all in capital letters tell us? that a character is saying something in a loud, raised voice

STOP **Have students to point to an exclamation mark.**

Ask: What does the exclamation mark tell us? that a character is saying something with a lot of expression and in a raised voice

Which character speaks more with words in all capital letters and exclamation marks, Boris or Morris? Boris

Why do you think Boris speaks in a loud, raised voice in so many parts of the story? because he's frustrated and angry with Morris

---

2

Ask: How do you think Boris says *no* here? with a lot of expression; in a raised voice
These words aren't written in all capital letters. How can you tell he's raising his voice? the exclamation marks

Have students reread the words *no no no* in an expressive, raised voice.

Read aloud pages 72–74.

STOP **On page 74, point to the first word at the top of the page and ask:** How do you think Boris says this word? in a really loud voice   How can you tell? It's in all capital letters; there's an exclamation mark.

How do you think Boris is feeling here? Possible answers: upset; angry; frustrated

Read aloud pages 75–78.

STOP **On page 78, point to** the last two lines.

Ask: How do you think Boris is saying the words here? in a raised voice; in an expressive voice   These words aren't in all capital letters. How can you tell he's raising his voice? the exclamation marks

Have students reread the last two lines on page 78 the way they think that Boris is saying them.

Open and fold back the page to see **3** .

Explore "Morris Has a Cold"
What It Sounds Like, What It Means

LITERATURE & COMPREHENSION

Draw a picture of what the words in the sentence sound like they mean.

> It's raining cats and dogs.

Draw a picture of what the words really mean.

Introduce *Amelia Bedelia*
What Does She Mean? Idioms

Fold the page into thirds so that the section labeled **1** is showing. Use an accordion, or Z, fold (see the diagram). Use this Reading Aid to read *Amelia Bedelia* with students.

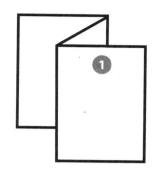

1

You will read *Amelia Bedelia* with students. Stop at the points indicated and follow the instructions.

Read aloud the book from the beginning to page 17.

Tell students that *change the towels* is an idiom.

Ask: What do you think Mrs. Rogers wants Amelia Bedelia to do with the bathroom towels? *take the old towels down and hang up clean ones*

What does Amelia think she's supposed to do? *make the towels look different*

Read aloud pages 18–21.

STOP Ask: What is the idiom on page 20? *dust the furniture*

What does Mrs. Rogers want Amelia to do? *take the dust off the furniture*

What does Amelia think she's supposed to do? *put dust on the furniture*

Read aloud pages 22–25.

Ask: What does Mrs. Rogers want Amelia to do? *close the drapes*

What does Amelia think she's supposed to do? *make a picture of the drapes*

Flip over to see **2**.

LITERATURE & COMPREHENSION

3

What do you think Mrs. Rogers will say next time she wants Amelia to change the towels? take down the old towels and put up different towels

What do you think Mrs. Rogers will say next time she wants Amelia to trim the fat on the steak? cut off the fat

What do you think Mrs. Rogers will say next time she wants Amelia to dress the chicken? get the chicken ready to cook

2

Read aloud pages 26–29.

STOP **Ask:** What idiom is on page 28? *put the lights out*

What does Mrs. Rogers want Amelia to do? turn off the lights

What does Amelia think she's supposed to do? take the light bulbs and put them outside

Read aloud pages 30–42.

Ask: What do you think *trim the fat* means? cut off the fat

What does Amelia think that it means? decorate the fat

Tell students that *dress the chicken* means to prepare it for cooking.

What does Amelia think it means? put clothes on it

Read aloud to the end of the book.

Ask: What is an idiom? a phrase that means something different than what it actually says

Why does Amelia Bedelia do things differently than Mrs. Rogers expects her to? because she does exactly what the words mean, not what the idioms mean

Open and fold back the page to see **3**.

Explore *Amelia Bedelia*
Multiple-Meaning Words in *Amelia Bedelia*

Fold the page into thirds so that the section labeled **1** is showing. Use an accordion, or Z, fold (see the diagram). Use this Reading Aid to read *Amelia Bedelia* with students.

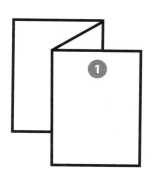

1

You will read *Amelia Bedelia* with students. Stop at the points indicated and follow the instructions.

STOP **Tell** students that *dust* has more than one meaning. It can mean the small bits of dirt that collect on furniture. It can also mean the action of cleaning small bits of dirt off the furniture.

Ask: Which word do you think is causing confusion for Amelia? *dust*

Read aloud the book from the beginning to page 21.

Ask: Which meaning does Mrs. Rogers have in mind when she asks Amelia to dust the furniture? clean small bits of dirt

What does Amelia think she's supposed to do? put bits of dirt on the furniture

Read aloud pages 22–26.

Ask: Which word is Amelia confused about? draw

What does Amelia think the word *draw* means here? to make a picture

What is the meaning of *draw* that Mrs. Rogers is using? to pull close

Flip over to see **2**.

3

Read aloud to the end of the book.

Ask: What are some of the words in the book that have
more than one meaning? Possible answers: *change; draw;
cup; trim*

What kind of problems do these words cause for Amelia
and Mrs. Rogers? Amelia uses one meaning of a word,
but Mrs. Rogers is thinking of a different meaning for the
same word.

2

Read aloud pages 28–35.

Ask: What kind of cup do you think
Mrs. Rogers is talking about when she says
to "measure two cups of rice," the kind we
use for ingredients when we're cooking
or the kind for drinking? the kind for
cooking   What kind of cup does Amelia
use? the kind for drinking

How does Amelia measure the rice? with a
measuring tape   How does Mrs. Rogers
expect Amelia to measure the rice? with a
measuring cup

Read aloud pages 36–41.

Ask: What does Mrs. Rogers ask Amelia
to do to the steak before she puts it in the
icebox? trim the fat   What does that
mean? cut off the fat

The word *trim* has more than one meaning.
What meaning do you think Mrs. Rogers
has in mind? cut

What does Amelia do to the steak? She
decorates it.   So what do you think is
another meaning of the word *trim*? to
decorate

Open and fold back the page to see **3**.

Explore *Amelia Bedelia*

What It Sounds Like, What It Means

Draw a picture to show how Amelia Bedelia would do **one** of these chores.

> - Trim the grass in the front yard.
> - Toss the salad.
> - Return the bat to the boy next door.

LITERATURE & COMPREHENSION

Explore Poems About the Weather (D)
Words That Convey Feelings

Fold the page into thirds so that the section labeled **1** is showing. Use an accordion, or Z, fold (see the diagram). Use this Reading Aid to examine the poem "No-Sweater Sun" in *Weather: Poems for All Seasons*.

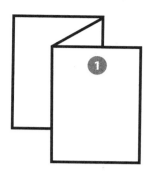

1

You will read "No-Sweater Sun" with students. Stop at the points indicated and follow the instructions.

Read aloud lines 1 and 2.

Ask: How do you think the poet was feeling when she wrote these lines? Answers will vary. Guide students to discuss positive feelings such as happiness and excitement.

Which words do you think help express those feelings? Answers will vary.

Read aloud lines 3 and 4.

Ask: How do you think the poet was feeling? Answers will vary. Guide students to discuss positive feelings such as happiness and excitement.

Flip over to see **2**.

2

Ask: How do you think the poet was
feeling when she wrote, "You *have* to run"?
Guide students to discuss feelings of
excitement.

How do you feel when you hear that line?
Answers will vary.

Read aloud to the end of the poem.

Ask: How do you think the poet was
feeling when she wrote these lines? Guide
students to discuss positive feelings such
as happiness and excitement.

How do those lines make you feel? Answers
will vary. Guide students to discuss positive
feelings such as happiness and excitement.

Which words help you feel that way?
Answers will vary. Guide students to
recognize that words such as *cartwheels,
sing, dizzy,* and *giddy* may cause them to
feel happy or excited.

How do you think the poet was feeling
when she wrote "No-Sweater Sun"? happy;
excited

How does the poem make you feel?
Answers will vary.

Which words in the poem make you feel
that way? Answers will vary.

Explore Poems About the Weather (D)
Imagine a Summer Day

Draw a picture of what you imagine when you hear the poem "On a Summer Day." Then, complete the sentence.

I imagine _____

_____ in my head.

Introduce "Our Earth in Space"
Words That Describe: Adjectives

Fold the page into thirds so that the section labeled ❶ is showing. Use an accordion, or Z, fold (see the diagram). Use this Reading Aid to read "Our Earth in Space" with students.

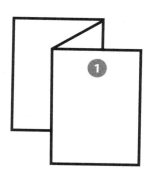

❶

You will read "Our Earth in Space" with students. Stop at the points indicated and follow the instructions.

Read aloud pages 50 and 51.

Ask: Did you hear a word that describes the shape of the earth?

Tell students that *flat* is an adjective that describes the earth. People once believed that the earth was flat. Now we know that the earth is round. The word *round* is an adjective, too.

Ask: Which word describes the earth? *beautiful*

Read aloud pages 52–54.

STOP Tell students that there are several adjectives on page 54. Have students reread the first paragraph on page 54 while tracking with their finger to practice fluent reading.

STOP Have students reread the second paragraph on page 54 while tracking with their finger to practice fluent reading.

Ask: In the sentence "We can see blue water," which word is an adjective that describes *water*? *blue*

Can you think of other words to describe *water*? Answers will vary.

Flip over to see ❷.

4

Read aloud to the end of the story.

STOP **Say:** Page 60 says that stars are "giant balls of fire." The word *giant* is an adjective. Can you think of other adjectives that describe stars? Answers will vary.

Ask: What do we call describing words? *adjectives*

What are some of the adjectives we read that describe the size of something? Possible answers: *big; bigger; giant; little; small; tiny*

How can we check if a word is an adjective? For example, if I want to describe the moon as *cold*, how can I be sure *cold* is an adjective? Put the word in front of *moon* and see if it makes sense. You can say *the cold moon*, so *cold* is an adjective.

What are some adjectives that we can use to describe the earth? Answers will vary.

Open and fold back the page to see **4**.

3

Explain that the story uses *big* to describe the sun. We can say, "The big sun," and it makes sense. So we know that *big* is an adjective.

Ask: Can you think of other words that describe the sun? Answers will vary.

Have students check if the words they suggest are adjectives by placing them in front of the word *sun*. For example, they can say, "The hot sun." *Hot* is an adjective.

Read aloud page 59.

STOP **Have students reread** the second paragraph on page 59 while tracking with their finger to practice fluent reading. Tell them to listen for words that describe what it's like on the sides of the earth.

Ask: Which adjective did you read that describes the side of the earth that faces the sun? *light*

Which adjective describes the other side of the earth? *dark*

2

Ask: In the sentence "We can see brown and green land," which adjectives describe *land*? *brown, green*

Ask: In the sentence "We can see fluffy white clouds," which adjectives describe *clouds*? *fluffy, white*

Can you think of other words to describe *clouds*? Answers will vary.

STOP **Tell** students that as they read the next few pages, they should listen for words that describe size.

Read aloud pages 56–58.

Ask: What adjectives did you hear that describe size? *bigger, little, big, small*

STOP **Tell** students that one way to check if a word is an adjective is to put it in front of the thing it is describing. For example, we can say, "The big earth." This makes sense, so we know that *big* is an adjective. But if we say, "The move earth," it does not make sense. So we know that *move* is **not** an adjective.

Open and fold back the page to see **3**.

Explore "Our Earth in Space"
"Our Earth in Space" Main Idea and Details

Fold the page into thirds so that the section labeled ① is showing. Use an accordion, or Z, fold (see the diagram). Use this Reading Aid to read "Our Earth in Space" with students.

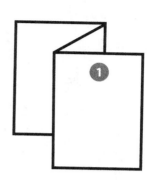

---

①

You will read "Our Earth in Space" with students. Stop at the points indicated and follow the instructions.

Read aloud the title.

Ask: What is this whole story about? the earth

Explain that since this story is all about the earth, we say that the topic is "the earth."

Say: This can be confusing when we are learning about the main idea. When we state the topic of a text or a paragraph, it sounds like a title with very few words, such as "the earth." But when we state the main idea, we say it in a sentence that states a complete thought, such as, "We know a lot more about the earth now than people did in the past." We will discuss this more as we read.

Read aloud pages 50–54.

STOP Say: I'm going to look carefully at the last paragraph on page 54 to figure out the main idea.

Have students reread the last paragraph on page 54 with you as they track with their finger.

Say: This paragraph has details about the many things that we can see if we look at the earth from out in space. I think that the main idea is, "We can see many things when we look at the earth." I can check this by looking at what each sentence in the paragraph says.

Flip over to see ②.

2

Ask: Does the sentence, "We can see blue water," tell us something we can see when we look at the earth? Yes

Can we see brown and green land, and fluffy white clouds when we look at the earth? Yes

Can we see that the earth is round? Yes

Say: All the sentences give supporting details about what we see when we look at the earth. So I just confirmed that the main idea of the last paragraph on page 54 is, "We can see many things when we look at the earth."

Read aloud pages 56–58.

STOP **Say:** Let's check whether the main idea of the paragraph on page 58 is, "The earth moves around the sun."

Ask: Does the sentence, "Now we know that the sun is very big," give information about how the earth moves around the sun? No

Does the sentence, "It is much, much bigger than the earth," give a detail about how the earth moves around the sun? No

Say: So I don't think the main idea is, "The earth moves around the sun," anymore. Now I think the main idea is, "Now we know a lot about the sun."

Open and fold back the page to see **3**.

3

Ask: Do the sentences in the paragraph on page 58 give details on what we know about the sun? Yes

What are some details in this paragraph on what we now know about the sun? Possible answers: It's very big; it's bigger than the earth; it looks small because it's far away; the sun doesn't move; the earth moves.

Say: This is a good paragraph to show the difference between the topic and the main idea. This paragraph on page 58 gives lots of details about the sun. We can say that the topic is "the sun." But the main idea is a complete sentence: "Now we know a lot about the sun."

Read aloud pages 59–65.

STOP **Say:** Let's figure out the main idea for the last paragraph of the story on page 65.

Have students reread the paragraph with you as they track with their finger.

Ask: What does most of this paragraph talk about? traveling in space

If students have trouble determining what the paragraph is about, suggest that it is about traveling in space.

Open and fold back the page to see **4**.

4

Say: I could say that "space travel" is the topic of this last paragraph because it sounds like a title and it isn't a complete thought. But, I want to state the main idea, and that needs to be a complete sentence.

Ask: How can we change "space travel" into a complete sentence so that we have a main idea? Guide students to state a complete sentence similar to the final sentence in the story.

If the main idea is, "Someday you might travel in space," what information or details in the paragraph on page 65 support that? Someday you might visit a planet; someday you might find out something new about the stars, the sun, or the moon.

Conclude by asking: What is a main idea? It's what a paragraph is mostly about.

How can I tell the difference between the main idea and the topic? The main idea is a complete sentence; the topic is more like a title, just one or two words.

What do we call the information in a paragraph that tells us about the main idea? details; supporting details

Explore "Our Earth in Space"
Main Idea and Details in the World Around Us

Fill in the chart. Write the main idea and two details for the picture.

Main idea

Details

Introduce "By the Light of the Moon"
What Did I Learn?

Complete the KWL chart.

Know What do we know?	Want What do we want to know?	Learn What did we learn?
The moon is round.	When did the first astronaut walk on the moon?	It takes about one month for the moon to go around the earth one time.

Introduce "By the Light of the Moon"
Words with Long *a* Spelling Patterns

Fold the page into thirds so that the section labeled ① is showing. Use an accordion, or Z, fold (see the diagram). Use this Reading Aid to read "By the Light of the Moon" with students.

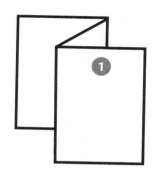

---

①

You will read "By the Light of the Moon" with students. Stop at the points indicated and follow the instructions.

Read aloud page 13.

Ask: Did you hear any words that have the long *a* sound? *maybe, neighbor, space, always, same, place, way*

STOP **Write** these words on index cards and set them aside to be sorted later in the activity.

Read aloud page 15, including the caption.

Ask: Which words have the long *a* sound? *shape(d), crater(s), they, space, state*

STOP **Write** any new words on index cards and set them aside.

Read aloud pages 16 and 17.

Ask: Which words have the long *a* sound? *place(s), always, face(s), shape, change, phase(s)*

STOP **Write** any new words on index cards and set them aside.

Read aloud page 18.

Ask: Which words have the long *a* sound? *always, take(s), same, phase(s), day*

Flip over to see **②**.

4

Ask: When you read and write words with the long *a* sound, do you think these words are more likely to be spelled with *ay* or with the silent *e* at the end? *with the silent e at the end*

Conclude by asking: When you are reading and you come across a word spelled with *ay*, what sound do those letters make? *long a*

When you come across a word spelled with an *a* and a silent *e* at the end, what sound does the *a* make? *long a*

3

Ask: Which words have the long *a* sound spelled with the letters *ay* as in *pay*? *maybe, always, way, day, may, someday*

Which words have the long *a* sound spelled with the silent *e* at the end as in *make*? *space, same, place, shape, crater, state, face, change, phase, take, made*

Which words have the long *a* spelled in a different way? *neighbor, they, weigh*

Explain that the spelling pattern *eigh* is another way to make the long *a* sound, but we don't see it as often as *ay* or the silent *e*. And *they* is a sight word that should be learned by heart. It does not have a spelling pattern that is regularly used for long *a*.

Ask: Can you think of any other words that were not in the story that have the long *a* sound? *Answers will vary.*

STOP **Write** words that students think of on index cards, and then have students sort these words into the groups of words from the story.

Open and fold back the page to see **4** .

2

STOP **Write** any new words on index cards.

Read aloud pages 20 and 21, including the captions.

Ask: Which words have the long *a* sound? *they, space, place, made, weigh, way*

Write any new words on index cards.

Read aloud page 22.

Ask: Which words have the long *a* sound? *may, neighbor, space, they, maybe, someday*

STOP **Tell** students that they are now going to sort the words.

Place the index cards with *pay* and *make* as headings for sorting. Write *other* on an index card and explain that it will be the heading for any words that do not fit into the other two groups.

Sort the words with students. Have students read each word and place it under the heading according to how the long *a* sound is spelled. All words spelled with *ay* should be placed under the heading *pay*. All words spelled with the silent *e* at the end should be placed under the heading *make*. Words that do not have these spelling patterns should be placed under *other*.

Open and fold back the page to see **3** .

Explore "By the Light of the Moon"

"By the Light of the Moon": Time-Order Words

Fold the page into thirds so that the section labeled ❶ is showing. Use an accordion, or Z, fold (see the diagram). Use this Reading Aid to read "By the Light of the Moon" with students.

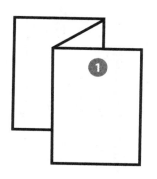

You will read "By the Light of the Moon" with students. Stop at the points indicated and follow the instructions.

· · · · · · · · · · · · · · · · · · · ·

Read aloud page 13.

Ask: Do you see anything on this page that is related to time? the calendar

Tell students that we can find references to time in the words of a text and in the text features.

Explain that the article says that it takes about one month for the moon to travel around the earth one time. If students are not sure what that means, the picture of the calendar page might help them understand what a month is.

STOP **Have students reread** the last paragraph on page 13 with you while they track with their finger.

Ask: If we see the full moon at the beginning of May and it takes about a month for the moon to go around the earth, when do you think we would see the next full moon? at the beginning of June

Read aloud pages 14 and 15.

STOP **Point to** and read the caption on page 14. Explain that 1600s refers to a time period about 400 years ago. This tells us that people have been studying the moon for a very long time, at least 400 years.

②

Read aloud pages 16 and 17.

STOP **Explain** that the text and text feature on pages 18 and 19 provide a lot of information about the order, or sequence, of the moon's phases. Tell students to listen carefully for words that indicate the order of events as they read pages 18 and 19 with you.

Read aloud pages 18 and 19.

Ask: What were some of the words you read that help us figure out the order in which things happen? *first, then, soon, at last*

Can you find the sentence that tells us which is the first phase of the moon? Students should indicate the sentence, "First is the new moon," in the second paragraph on page 18.

STOP **Point to** the diagram of the moon's phases on pages 18 and 19.

Ask: How does this diagram show the order, or sequence, of the moon's phases? The arrows show how the phases follow each other.

Do the phases of the moon happen only once or over and over? over and over

How do you know that the phases of the moon happen over and over? The pictures of the phases of the moon and the arrows go in a circle that keeps going around.

Open and fold back the page to see **③**.

③

Read aloud pages 20 and 21.

Explain that a text can tell us when something happened by giving a year.

Ask: What year did astronauts first travel to the moon? 1969

Earlier, the article says that Galileo looked at the moon through a telescope in the 1600s. Which happened first: Galileo looking at the moon, or astronauts traveling to the moon? Galileo looking at the moon   How do you know? Galileo looking at the moon: because the 1600s happened before 1969

Read aloud pages 22 and 23.

Explain that the text on page 22 does not have any time-order words or years, but it does refer to time in another way.

STOP **Have students reread** the last paragraph on page 22 with you as they track with their finger.

Ask: What does this paragraph say might happen in the future? Maybe you will visit the moon someday; maybe you will help answer questions about the moon.

Explain that when a text uses words like *will* and *someday*, it is talking about things that could happen in the future. These words are another way that a text can indicate time.

Open and fold back the page to see **④**.

④

Conclude by asking: What are some of the ways that this article refers to time and the order that things happen? Possible answers: with words like *first* and *last*; with years; with pictures of the moon's phases

What are some of the words we can use to tell the sequence, or order that things happen in? Possible answers: *first; next; then; soon; last*

What are some words that let us know a text is talking about something that could happen in the future? words such as *will* and *someday*

Explore "By the Light of the Moon"
Make a Magazine Page

Cut out the text features. Then, glue them on blank paper to make your own magazine page.

Astronauts must wear special suits when they walk on the moon. These suits are called space suits. Space suits keep astronauts warm when the moon gets very cold. The suits also keep astronauts cool when the moon gets very hot. Space suits have air for astronauts to breathe and a way for them to talk to the spacecraft.

A special car was built for astronauts to drive on the moon. It is called a moon rover.

Astronauts on the Moon

Dressed Just Right

LITERATURE & COMPREHENSION

Introduce "The *Eagle* on the Moon"
Book Walk with 5 Ws and H

Fill in the blanks with questions about "The *Eagle* on the Moon."

1. Who _____

   _____

   _____?

2. What _____

   _____

   _____?

3. Where _____

   _____

   _____?

LITERATURE & COMPREHENSION

4. When _____

_____

_____?

5. Why _____

_____

_____?

6. How _____

_____

_____?

Introduce "The *Eagle* on the Moon"
Capital Letters

Cut out the sentence strips, and tape them together.

1. They needed

2. expert pilots

3. like Mike, Neil,

4. and Buzz.

Introduce "The *Eagle* on the Moon"
Capital Letters

Fold the page into thirds so that the section labeled ❶ is showing. Use an accordion, or Z, fold (see the diagram). Use this Reading Aid to read "The *Eagle* on the Moon" with students.

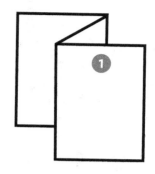

❶

You will read "The *Eagle* on the Moon" with students. Stop at the points indicated and follow the instructions.

Read aloud page 25.

Ask: Can you point to any words in the first paragraph that begin with capital letters? Students should point to *Outer, Different, They, Who, How,* and *It.* Why do these words begin with capitals? They are at the beginning of sentences.

Which words in the last sentence on the page begin with capital letters? *So, United States,* and *American*

STOP **Tell** students that *United States* is the specific name of a place. *America* also names a specific place, while *American* is the specific name of a person that lives there. All these words are proper nouns, so they are capitalized. *So* is capitalized because it begins the sentence.

Read aloud page 26 and 27, including the caption.

STOP **Point to** the word *No* at the beginning of the first sentence on page 26. Explain that this word is capitalized because it is at the beginning of a sentence.

Have students point to another example of a word that is capitalized because it begins a sentence.

Flip over to see ❷.

2

STOP **Point to** the words *Neil Armstrong* in the second paragraph on page 26. Explain that these words are capitalized because they are proper nouns. In this case, they are the specific name of a person.

Have students point to another example of words that are capitalized because they are the specific name of a person. Students should point to *Mike Collins* or *Buzz Aldrin*.

Read aloud pages 28–31.

STOP **Point to** the word *July* at the top of page 31.

Ask: Why does this word begin with a capital letter? It's a proper noun; it's the specific name of a month.

Read aloud page 32.

STOP **Point to** the word *Eagle* in the first sentence on page 32.

Ask: Why does this word begin with a capital letter? It's a proper noun; it's the specific name of the ship that took the astronauts to the moon's surface.

Open and fold back the page to see **3** .

3

Read aloud pages 34 and 35, including the captions.

STOP **Point to** the word *July* at the top of page 34.
Tell students that it begins with a capital letter because it's the specific name of a month.

Have students point to another example of a word that is capitalized because it is the specific name of a month. Students should point to *July* in the caption on page 35.

Have students point to an example of words that are capitalized because they are the specific name of a person. Students should point to *Neil Armstrong* or *Buzz Aldrin* on page 34.

STOP **Point to** the words *Pacific Ocean* on page 35.

Ask: Why do these words begin with capital letters? They're a proper noun; they're the specific name of a place.

Read aloud pages 36 and 37.

Ask: What are the reasons that a word would start with a capital letter? It's a proper noun; it's at the beginning of a sentence; it's the name of a specific person, place, or month.

Have students point to an example of a word that is capitalized because it's the specific name of a month. Students should point to *July* on page 37.

Open and fold back the page to see **4** .

4

STOP **Conclude** by having students fluently read the sentence on the sentence strip while tracking with their finger.

Point to the word *They*.

Ask: Why does this word begin with a capital letter? It's the beginning of a sentence.

Point to the word *Mike*.

Ask: Why does this word begin with a capital letter? It's a proper noun; it's the specific name of a person.

Have students point to another example of words that are capitalized because they are the specific name of a person. Students should point to *Neil* or *Buzz*.

If time allows, have students demonstrate their understanding of sentence structure. Cut apart the sentence on the sentence strip so that each word is separate. Mix up the words, and then have students rebuild the sentence with the words in the correct order.

Explore "The *Eagle* on the Moon"

"The *Eagle* on the Moon": Sequence

Fold the page into thirds so that the section labeled **1** is showing. Use an accordion, or Z, fold (see the diagram). Use this Reading Aid to read "The *Eagle* on the Moon" with students.

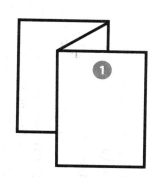

1

You will read "The *Eagle* on the Moon" with students. Stop at the points indicated and follow the instructions.

. . . .

Read aloud pages 24 and 25.

Ask: Did you notice a reference to years? What years does the article mention?

Yes   the 1960s

Explain that when the article says "the 1960s," that means the events happened during the time from 1960 through 1969.

STOP **Have students reread** the second and third paragraphs on page 25 with you as they track with their finger.

Ask: Did you hear any of the signal words that help tell the sequence of events? *first* and *soon*

Who sent a man to space first? the Russians

The article then says that *soon* something else happened. What happened soon after the Russians sent a man to space? The first American astronaut went to space.

Flip over to see **2**.

4

Read aloud the time line on pages 36 and 37.

Ask: What is the text feature on pages 36 and 37 with the pictures and dates called? a time line

Explain that a time line lists important events and the years in which they happened, all organized in sequence. Since a time line includes the years in order, we say that it is organized in chronological order.

Ask: What is the first year mentioned on the time line? 1961   According to the time line, what happened in that year? A Russian man was sent into space.

Conclude by asking: When an article has the important events described in the order in which they happened, how do we say the article is organized? in sequence

What are some of the clues in this article that helped us figure out that it is organized in sequence? Possible answers: It has years in it; it has signal words like *first, then, last;* it talks about important events in the order that they happened.

3

Read aloud pages 34 and 35.

STOP **Ask:** What date is mentioned on page 34? July 20, 1969   What happened on that date? The astronauts walked on the moon.

Is this date before or after the date the men started their trip to the moon, July 16, 1969? after

Explain that the article says the men returned to the earth four days later.

STOP **Have students reread** the last paragraph on page 34 with you as they track with their finger.

Explain that we can figure out the sequence of events and when important events happened when we have phrases such as *four days later.*

Say: If the astronauts landed on the moon on July 20 and they returned to the earth four days later, what date did they return to the earth? July 24   How can we figure that out? Add 4 to 20.

Open and fold back the page to see **4** .

2

Read aloud pages 26–29.

STOP **Ask:** Did you hear a year mentioned on page 28? Yes, 1968

Based on what we've read so far, what happened first: Did the Russians send a man into space, or did the American astronauts get picked to go to the moon? The Russians sent a man into space.

Read aloud pages 30 and 31.

STOP **Ask:** What date is mentioned on page 31? July 16, 1969   What happened on that date? The astronauts started their trip to the moon.

Did this happen before or after the Russians first sent a man into space? after

Read aloud pages 32 and 33.

STOP **Explain** that page 32 describes the astronauts' trip from the big ship to the moon in a smaller ship called the *Eagle.*

Ask: What was the first thing that the astronauts did according to the section of the article "Flying the *Eagle*"? Neil and Buzz climbed into the *Eagle.*

Open and fold back the page to see **3** .

● Explore "The *Eagle* on the Moon"
Land the *Eagle* on the Moon

1. Cut out the pictures.
2. Put the pictures in the order that they happen in the article.
3. Glue the pictures in order.

He found a safe spot to land just in time. The *Eagle* was on the moon.

Soon, the *Eagle* was on its way to the moon.

Then, something went wrong. The *Eagle* was heading straight for some rocks.

Neil and Buzz climbed into a small ship called the *Eagle*.

Neil took charge. He steered the ship away from the rocks. But, he had to hurry. The *Eagle* was running out of fuel.

Glue the pictures in the order that they happen in "The *Eagle* on the Moon."

Introduce "Women in Space"
Chronological Order

Fold the page into thirds so that the section labeled ❶ is showing. Use an accordion, or Z, fold (see the diagram). Use this Reading Aid to read "Women in Space" with students.

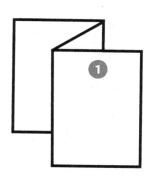

❶

You will read "Women in Space" with students. Stop at the points indicated and follow the instructions.

· · · · · · · · · · · · · · · ·

Read aloud pages 38 and 39.

Ask: Did the paragraphs on these pages mention any years? Yes   What years? 1961 and 1978

STOP **Have students reread** page 38 with you as they track with their finger.

Ask: What happened in 1961? The first astronauts went to space.

STOP **Write** 1961 and what happened that year on an index card. Set the card aside for later use.

Explain that the first astronauts were all men. But 17 years after the first astronauts went to space, women finally were able to become astronauts.

Ask: What year did that happen? 1978

STOP **Write** 1978 and what happened that year on an index card. Set the card aside for later use.

Read aloud page 40.

Ask: Did the paragraphs on this page mention a year? Yes   What year? 1983

Flip over to see ❷.

4

STOP **Tell** students that they will now make a time line by arranging the index cards in order.

Have students read the year on each card and place the cards in chronological order with 1961 at the left end of the time line and 2004 at the right end.

Read aloud the year and events described on each index card in the order they happened.

Have students reread the time line while tracking with their finger and matching their voice to the print. Encourage them to read as fluently as possible.

Explain that the sections of the article about Sally Ride and Kathryn Sullivan are written in chronological order. Our time line is also arranged in chronological order. So we can easily see the order in which important events happened and when they happened.

Conclude by asking: What is the first event on our time line? 1961—the first astronauts went to space.

When an article mentions important events and the years that those events happened in order, how do we say the article is organized? in chronological order

---

3

STOP **Write** 1984 on an index card. Have students describe the important events of that year and write them on the card. Students should mention that Sally Ride and Kathryn Sullivan went to space, and Kathryn did a space walk.

Read aloud the caption on page 43.

Ask: What happened in 2004? Kathryn Sullivan became part of the Astronaut Hall of Fame.

STOP **Write** 2004 and what happened that year on an index card.

Read aloud pages 44–47.

Ask: Does the article mention any years on these pages? No

Explain that pages 44–47 tell us about other women astronauts. They tell us the events in those astronauts' lives and the order that they happened, but they don't mention any years. So we won't be able to add events from these astronauts' lives to our time line.

Read aloud pages 48 and 49.

Explain that these pages are the end, or conclusion, of the article.

Ask: Does the conclusion of the article mention any years? No

Open and fold back the page to see **4** .

2

STOP **Have students reread** the second paragraph on page 40 with you as they track with their finger.

Ask: What happened in 1983? Sally Ride became the first American woman in space.

STOP **Write** 1983 and what happened that year on an index card. Set the card aside for later use.

Read aloud page 42.

Explain that there is no year mentioned on this page. But we can figure out in what year the events described on this page happened.

STOP **Have students reread** the first sentence on page 42 with you as they track with their finger.

Ask: Sally Ride first went to space in 1983. The article says that she went to space again the next year. What is the next year after 1983? 1984

Who went to space with Sally that year? Kathryn Sullivan   What was Kathryn's special job on this trip? to do a space walk

Open and fold back the page to see **3** .

Explore "Women in Space"
Facts and Opinions

Look at the pictures.

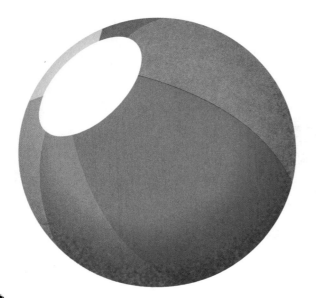

beach ball

basketball

Explore "Women in Space"

"Women in Space": Repair Comprehension

Fold the page into thirds so that the section labeled ❶ is showing. Use an accordion, or Z, fold (see the diagram). Use this Reading Aid to read "Women in Space" with students.

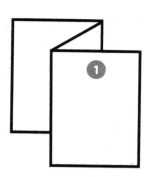

You will read "Women in Space" with students. Stop at the points indicated and follow the instructions.

Read aloud pages 38 and 39.

Say: I'm confused. I don't know what NASA is. I'm going to reread the first paragraph of page 38 and ask myself, "What is NASA?"

STOP **Have students reread** the first paragraph of page 38 with you as they track with their finger.

Say: I see that NASA is in bold type, so I can look it up in the back of the magazine to find out what it is.

STOP Look up NASA in the glossary on page 51 and read the definition aloud.

Say: So NASA must be the organization that the astronauts work for. That must be why women couldn't become astronauts for so long. NASA wouldn't let them, and NASA is in charge of space travel.

Read aloud page 40.

Say: I didn't understand the part about what Sally did when she was in space. I'm going to reread that part and ask myself, "What was Sally's job in space?"

Flip over to see ❷.

❶

2

STOP **Have students reread** the third paragraph of page 40 with you as they track with their finger.

Ask: What did the paragraph say about Sally's job in space? She did experiments; she tested a machine that could put things into space and catch things in space to bring into the shuttle.

Read aloud pages 42 and 43.

Say: I didn't understand the part about Kathryn walking in space. I think I'm going to reread that part and ask myself, "What is a space walk?"

STOP **Have students reread** the second paragraph of page 42 with you as they track with their finger.

Say: I see that *space walk* is in bold type, so I can look up the definition in the back of the magazine.

STOP Look up *space walk* in the glossary on page 52 and read the definition aloud.

Open and fold back the page to see **3** .

3

Say: Now I understand that Kathryn must have gone outside of the shuttle to do some work. She wasn't really walking because she would have been floating in space. She must have been attached to the shuttle somehow so that she wouldn't float away.

Read aloud pages 44 and 45.

Say: I don't understand why Mae couldn't become an astronaut. I'm going to reread this part and ask myself, "Why couldn't Mae become an astronaut?"

STOP **Have students reread** the first two paragraphs of page 45 with you as they track with their finger.

Say: Now I see that the article says that people thought that Mae could never be an astronaut. I know that's an opinion, not a fact, because of the word *thought*. So Mae could become an astronaut.

Read aloud pages 46 and 47.

Say: I don't remember what Ellen Ochoa's job was. So I'm going to reread this part.

STOP **Have students reread** the first paragraph of page 46 with you as they track with their finger.

Ask: What was Ellen's job? scientist; inventor

Open and fold back the page to see **4** .

4

STOP **Tell** students that when they reread the last pages with you, you want them to practice reading fluently.

Read aloud pages 48 and 49 as students track with their finger.

Conclude by asking: What can you do if you realize that you don't understand something you just read? You can reread; you can ask yourself a question about what you're trying to figure out and then reread.

Explore "Women in Space"
How Do They Compare?

Fill in the chart to compare and contrast two astronauts.

	Neil Armstrong	Sally Ride
Year became an astronaut?		
First year in space?		
Went to space more than once?		
Why important?		

LITERATURE & COMPREHENSION

Fact about Neil Armstrong: _____

_____

_____

Opinion about Neil Armstrong: _____

_____

_____

Fact about Sally Ride: _____

_____

_____

Opinion about Sally Ride: _____

_____

_____

Introduce "The Pine Tree and Its Needles"
Who's Talking?

Fold the page into thirds so that the section labeled **1** is showing. Use an accordion, or Z, fold (see the diagram). Use this Reading Aid to read "The Pine Tree and Its Needles" with students.

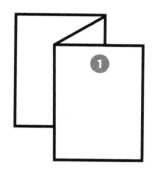

You will read "The Pine Tree and Its Needles" with students. Stop at the points indicated and follow the instructions.

Read aloud paragraphs 1 and 2.

Ask: Who is speaking aloud? the little pine tree

What does the little pine tree say? "I do not like my green needles. I wish I had beautiful leaves. How happy I should be if only I had gold leaves!"

STOP **Point to** the quotation marks.

Say: We can tell that a character is speaking when we see quotation marks. Quotation marks always come in pairs. The words inside the quotation marks are what a character says aloud.

Read aloud paragraph 3.

Ask: Can you point to the quotation marks in this paragraph? Students should point to the quotation marks.

Who is speaking? the Fairy

What does the Fairy say? "Little pine tree, you may have your wish."

Flip over to see **2**.

3

STOP **Tell** students that you will read aloud the story to the end. They will help you by pretending to be the characters in the story and reading aloud what the characters say. You will read all the other words.

Ask: Which words will you read aloud? the words inside the quotation marks

Will you read aloud the words *it said* or *she said?* No Why not? because the characters don't say those words aloud; because the characters don't say the words that are outside the quotation marks

Read aloud the rest of the story.

Ask students to point to quotation marks in the story.

Ask: What do the quotation marks tell us? that a character is speaking aloud

What is another clue that a character is speaking aloud? the word *said*

2

STOP **Point to** the words *she said.*

Explain that the word *said* is another clue that a character is speaking aloud.

Read aloud paragraphs 4–7.

Ask: Who is speaking now? the little pine tree   How do you know the little tree is speaking aloud? quotation marks; the word *said*

STOP **Point to** the opening quotation mark at the beginning of paragraph 5.

Tell students that when we see an opening quotation mark, we know that the first word a character will say is the word right after that quotation mark.

Ask: In the sentence *"What shall I do?"* it *said,* what is the last word that the little tree says aloud? *do*

Does the little tree say the words *it said?* No   How do you know? The quotation mark after the word *do* tells us that the little tree has stopped talking.

Open and fold back the page to see **3** .

Introduce "The Pine Tree and Its Needles"
From First to Last

1. Cut out the pictures.
2. Put the pictures in the order that they happen in the story.
3. Glue the pictures in order.

Glue the pictures in the order that they happen in "The Pine Tree and Its Needles."

Explore "The Pine Tree and Its Needles"
"The Pine Tree and Its Needles": Exclamation Marks

Cut out the sentence strips.

How beautiful I am. ❶

How beautiful I am! ❷

LITERATURE & COMPREHENSION

Explore "The Pine Tree and Its Needles"

"The Pine Tree and Its Needles": Exclamation Marks

Fold the page into thirds so that the section labeled **1** is showing. Use an accordion, or Z, fold (see the diagram). Use this Reading Aid to read "The Pine Tree and Its Needles" with students.

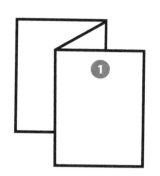

You will read "The Pine Tree and Its Needles" with students. Stop at the points indicated and follow the instructions.

....

Read aloud page 174.

Point to the last paragraph on page 174, which starts with *In the morning.*

Say: I see several exclamation marks here. That tells me the little pine tree is very excited and speaks with a lot of expression here.

STOP Have students reread the last paragraph on page 174 as they track with their finger. They should read the exclamations with a lot of expression and excitement.

Read aloud page 175.

Ask: Do you see any exclamation marks on this page? Yes   Should we read the sentences with exclamation marks in a normal voice or with excitement? with excitement

STOP Have students reread the last paragraph on page 175 as they track with their finger. They should read the exclamations with expression and excitement.

Flip over to see **2***.*

1

2

Read aloud page 176.

Ask: Is there an exclamation on this page? Yes Which sentence should we read with excitement and a lot of expression? *Oh, how it blew!*

STOP **Have students reread** the first paragraph on page 176 as they track with their finger. They should read the exclamation with expression and excitement.

Read aloud page 177.

Ask: Is there an exclamation on this page? Yes Which sentence should we read with excitement and a lot of expression? *How beautiful I am!*

STOP **Have students reread** the second paragraph on page 177 as they track with their finger. They should read the exclamation with expression and excitement.

STOP **Tell** students that there are no more exclamations on the last page of the story. Tell them that as they read the last page of the story, you would like them to practice reading fluently as they track with their finger.

Open and fold back the page to see **3** .

3

Read aloud page 178.

STOP **Show** students the sentence strips again.

Ask: How should we read each of these sentences? We should read the one that ends with a period in a normal voice. We should read the one that ends with the exclamation mark with a lot of expression and excitement.

Can you point to an exclamation mark somewhere in the story? Students should point to an exclamation mark on page 174, 175, 176, or 177.

What do we call a sentence that ends with an exclamation mark? an exclamation

What should we do when we're reading and we see an exclamation? read it with expression and excitement

STOP **If time allows,** have students demonstrate their understanding of sentence structure. Cut apart one of the sentences on the sentence strips so that each word is separate. Mix up the words, and then have students rebuild the sentence with the words in the correct order.

Introduce "The Little Rabbit Who Wanted Red Wings"

Words That Describe: Adjectives

Fold the page into thirds so that the section labeled **1** is showing. Use an accordion, or Z, fold (see the diagram). Use this Reading Aid to read "The Little Rabbit Who Wanted Red Wings" with students.

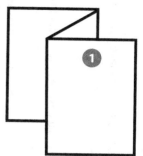

1

You will read "The Little Rabbit Who Wanted Red Wings" with students. Stop at the points indicated and follow the instructions.

Tell students to listen carefully for describing words at the beginning of the story, because there are many adjectives in the first two paragraphs.

Read aloud the first two paragraphs of page 180.

Ask: Which words describe Little Rabbit's fur? *soft; white*

Tell students that *soft* and *white* are adjectives.

Ask: Which adjectives describe Little Rabbit's ears, eyes, and tail? *long; pink; shiny; red; puffy*

STOP **Have students reread** the second paragraph on page 180 as they track with their finger.

Ask: Which adjectives in this paragraph describe the animals that Little Rabbit sees? *big; bushy; pointy; floppy; orange*

*Flip over to see **2**.*

(4)

Conclude by asking: What do we call describing words? adjectives

What are some of the adjectives we read in the story that describe the color of something? Possible answers: *white; pink; red*

How can we check if a word is an adjective? For example, if I want to describe the rabbit as *young*, how can I be sure *young* is an adjective? Put the word in front of *rabbit* and see if it makes sense. You can say, "the young rabbit," so *young* is an adjective.

What are some adjectives in the story that describe Little Rabbit? Possible answers: *tired; cold; hungry; soft; long; shiny; puffy*

---

(3)

Ask: Does it make sense if I say, "the hungry rabbit"? Yes What kind of word is *hungry*? an adjective

Ask: Can you think of other adjectives that could describe the little rabbit in the story? Answers will vary. If students have trouble answering, suggest words such as *silly, unhappy,* and *sad*.

Have students check if the words they suggest are adjectives by placing them in front of the word *rabbit*. For example, they can say, "the gray rabbit." *Gray* is an adjective.

Read aloud page 183.

Say: I noticed that Groundhog is very kind to Little Rabbit in the story. *Kind* is an adjective that describes Groundhog.

Ask: Can you think of other adjectives that could describe Groundhog? Possible answers: *friendly; helpful; nice; caring*

Open and fold back the page to see **(4)**.

---

(2)

Read aloud the rest of page 180 and page 181.

Ask: What color is the bird? red

What kind of word is the word *red*? an adjective; a describing word

Can you use the adjective *red* in a sentence? Answers will vary.

Read aloud page 182.

Tell students that you heard some adjectives that describe how Little Rabbit feels at this point in the story.

STOP **Have students reread** the third paragraph on page 182 as they track with their finger.

Ask: Which words tell us how Little Rabbit feels? *tired; cold; hungry*

STOP **Tell** students that one way to check whether a word is an adjective is to put it in front of the thing it is describing. For example, we can say, "the tired rabbit." This makes sense, so we know that *tired* is an adjective. But if we say, "the hop rabbit," it does not make sense. So we know that *hop* is **not** an adjective.

Open and fold back the page to see **(3)**.

Explore "The Little Rabbit Who Wanted Red Wings"

"The Little Rabbit Who Wanted Red Wings": Make Inferences

Fold the page into thirds so that the section labeled **1** is showing. Use an accordion, or Z, fold (see the diagram). Use this Reading Aid to read "The Little Rabbit Who Wanted Red Wings" with students.

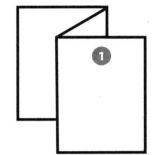

1

You will read "The Little Rabbit Who Wanted Red Wings" with students. Stop at the points indicated and follow the instructions.
....

Read aloud page 180.

Say: After reading this page, I'm getting an idea of what Little Rabbit is like. I can infer that Little Rabbit doesn't always listen to other people and that he wants to figure things out for himself. There are some clues in the story that led me to infer this. For example, his mother tells him that she loves him the way he is, but he still goes to the Wishing Pond to try to change himself. I also thought about people I know who are like this. You can offer them suggestions, but they usually won't follow those suggestions. They want to try things, even if other people think it's not a good idea.

Read aloud page 181.

Say: I wonder if Little Rabbit thought carefully before he made his wish.

Tell students that we can't know for sure whether Little Rabbit thought things through carefully, because the story doesn't tell us. But we can infer whether he thought carefully or not.

STOP **Have students reread** page 181 as they track with their finger. As they read, they should think about whether Little Rabbit thought carefully before making his wish.

2

Ask: Do you think Little Rabbit thought carefully before he made his wish? Answers will vary.

Can you think aloud and explain to me what clues in the story or from your own experiences helped you infer that? Answers will vary. Students are more likely to infer that Little Rabbit did not think carefully. Students may share information from earlier in the story about Little Rabbit wishing for different things every time he sees a different animal; students may have noticed that Little Rabbit had not wished for red wings before he got to the Wishing Pond. He made the wish right when he saw the bird, so he probably did not think it through.

STOP If students infer that Little Rabbit **did** think carefully before making his wish for red wings, be sure that they explain the reasons for their inference. Then explain to students the clues that might lead a reader to infer differently, that Little Rabbit did **not** think carefully.

STOP **Point to** Rabbit's face in the picture on page 181.

Open and fold back the page to see **3** *.*

3

Ask: Can you infer how Little Rabbit feels when he first gets his red wings? Possible answers: *happy; excited* Why did you infer that? Answers will vary. Students should notice that Little Rabbit is smiling in the picture. They should know from prior experience that they smile when they are happy or excited about something.

Read aloud page 182.

Tell students that the story never says what Groundhog is like, but we can make inferences based on his actions up to this point of the story.

Ask: How would you describe Groundhog? Possible answers: *friendly; helpful; nice; caring*

Can you think aloud and explain why you inferred that? Answers will vary. Students may share information about Groundhog's actions toward Little Rabbit, such as telling him about the Wishing Pond, taking him home for the night, and helping him get out of a sticker bush.

Ask: Does the story tell us how Little Rabbit's mother feels the night that he doesn't come home? No Based on your experiences with family and friends, what can you infer about how Little Rabbit's mother might feel when he doesn't come home? Possible answers: *worried; upset; scared*

Open and fold back the page to see **4** *.*

4

Read aloud page 183.

Ask: Does the story tell us why Little Rabbit hops home as fast as he can after his red wings disappear? No Can we infer this? Yes

Why do you think Little Rabbit hops home so fast? Answers will vary. Students are likely to infer that Little Rabbit missed his mother or that Little Rabbit is excited to show his mother that the wings are gone.

How do you think Little Rabbit and his mother feel at the end of the story? Possible answers: *happy; relieved* How did you infer that? Answers will vary. Students are likely to point out that Little Rabbit and his mother are smiling in the picture on page 183. They may also share personal experiences of feeling happy when they see a family member after being away for a while or feeling relieved when a bad experience is over.

Conclude by asking: What kind of information did you use to make inferences as we read the story again? Possible answers: information in the story; in the pictures; from personal experience

Explore "The Little Rabbit Who Wanted Red Wings"

Little Rabbit Gets All His Wishes

Draw or glue down items to show what Little Rabbit would look like if he got all his wishes.

LITERATURE & COMPREHENSION

Introduce "The Country Mouse and the City Mouse"

When Is the Story Happening?

Fold the page into thirds so that the section labeled ① is showing. Use an accordion, or Z, fold (see the diagram). Use this Reading Aid to read "The Country Mouse and the City Mouse" with students.

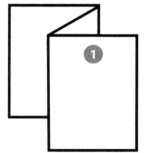

You will read "The Country Mouse and the City Mouse" with students. Stop at the points indicated and follow the instructions.

Read aloud the first two paragraphs on page 184.

Ask: Is the story happening now or in the past? in the past

Explain that we can tell the story happens in the past because of the words *was* and *came*. If the story were happening now, then these paragraphs would say, "There is a mouse. She lives in the country. One day her cousin comes to see her. She lives in the city."

STOP **Tell** students that as you read the rest of the story together, they should look for the action words, or verbs, that tell us that the story happens in the past.

Read aloud all of page 184.

Ask: Which words did you hear that tell us the story happens in the past? Possible answers: *was; lived; came; asked; said; looked; took; helped*

Flip over to see ② .

①

2

Read aloud page 185.

Ask: Which action words did you hear on this page that tell us the story happens in the past? Possible answers: *said; went; got; ran; looked; found*

Read aloud the first paragraph on page 186.

Ask: Which action words, or verbs, did you hear that tell us the story happens in the past? Possible answers: *heard; asked; whispered*

Explain that the verb *heard* in the phrase *they heard a terrible noise* tells us about something in the past. But if the story were happening now, the phrase would say *they hear a terrible noise.*

Read aloud the rest of page 186.

Ask: Which action words, or verbs, did you hear that tell us the story happens in the past? Possible answers: *ran; asked; said; went*

Explain that the verb *ran* in the sentence *Both mice ran* tells us that something is in the past.

Ask: If the story were happening now, how would the sentence *Both mice ran* be changed? *It would be Both mice run.*

Open and fold back the page to see **3***.*

3

Read aloud page 187.

Ask: Which verbs did you hear on this page that tell us the story happens in the past? Possible answers: *said; asked; looked*

What would we change the verb *asked* to if the story were happening now? *ask or asks*

Conclude by asking: Which words in a story tell us when a story is happening? the action words; the verbs

What are some of the verbs we heard in this story that helped us figure out that the story happens in the past? Students should name some of the verbs previously indicated.

Explore "The Country Mouse and the City Mouse"

"The Country Mouse and the City Mouse": Repair Comprehension

Fold the page into thirds so that the section labeled ❶ is showing. Use an accordion, or Z, fold (see the diagram). Use this Reading Aid to read "The Country Mouse and the City Mouse" with students.

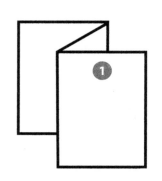

❶

You will read "The Country Mouse and the City Mouse" with students. Stop at the points indicated and follow the instructions.

Read aloud the first three paragraphs on page 184.

Say: I'm confused. I see the words *country* and *city,* so I'm not sure where the story is happening at the beginning.

STOP **Have students reread** the first three paragraphs on page 184 with you as they track with their finger.

Say: Now I see that the City Mouse is visiting her cousin, the Country Mouse. So the beginning of the story must be happening at the Country Mouse's house.

Read aloud the rest of page 184.

Say: I'm not sure why the Country Mouse doesn't have the same kinds of food that the City Mouse is used to eating. Let's use our prior knowledge to help us figure this out.

Ask: What kind of food does the Country Mouse have? beans and corn   Where do beans and corn grow? on farms

Explain that we know that farms are in the country. So that's probably why the Country Mouse has that kind of food, and not cake and cheese like the City Mouse.

Flip over to see ❷.

3

STOP **Tell** students that when they read the last page with you, you want them to practice reading fluently.

Read aloud page 187 as students track with their finger.

Ask: Is there anything on this page that you are confused about?

STOP If students indicate that they are confused, help them determine which strategy might help them clear up their confusion—rereading or thinking about their prior knowledge.

Conclude by asking: What strategies can you use if you realize that you don't understand something you just read? You can reread; you can use your prior knowledge to help you figure out something that is confusing.

2

Read aloud page 185.

Say: Some people might be confused about why the mice go to the kitchen when they arrive at the City Mouse's house. Let's see if we can use our prior knowledge to help us figure this out.

Ask: How are the mice feeling when they arrive in the city? hungry Where do people usually keep food? in the kitchen

Explain that from our prior knowledge, we know that there is usually food in a kitchen. So we can better understand why the mice go to the kitchen—they're hungry and they want to find some food.

Read aloud page 186.

Say: I'm a little confused about why the mice run away from the cat. Let's reread this page to figure it out.

STOP **Have students reread** page 185 with you as they track with their finger.

Ask: Why do the mice run away? The cat would eat the mice if it caught them.

Open and fold back the page to see **3** *.*

Explore "The Country Mouse and the City Mouse"

Who, Where, What

Complete the story map. Retell the story.

Characters	Setting

Title
"The Country Mouse and the City Mouse"

Plot

Beginning of story	Middle of story	End of story

Introduce "The Cap that Mother Made"

Punctuation in "The Cap that Mother Made"

Fold the page into thirds so that the section labeled ❶ is showing. Use an accordion, or Z, fold (see the diagram). Use this Reading Aid to read "The Cap that Mother Made" with students.

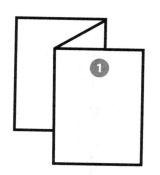

❶

You will read "The Cap that Mother Made" with students. Stop at the points indicated and follow the instructions.

Read aloud pages 188 and 189.

Ask: Did you see periods on these pages?
Yes   What should we do when we see a period? take a brief pause

STOP **Have students reread** the last paragraph on page 189 as they track with their finger. Make sure that students pause at every period.

STOP **Tell** students that as they read the next page, they should look for other punctuation marks in addition to periods.

Read aloud page 190.

Ask: Did you notice that somebody is talking on this page? Yes   Who is speaking? the farmer

What punctuation tells us that somebody is talking? quotation marks

What is the first word that the farmer says? well

Flip over to see ❷.

2

STOP If students are uncertain about which words the farmer says, remind them that quotation marks always come in pairs. Show students the words *Well, well, if it isn't my friend Anders* that are inside the quotation marks. Explain that the words inside the quotation marks are the words that a character says aloud.

Read aloud page 191.

Ask: What punctuation marks did you see on this page? a period; quotation marks

Who speaks on this page? Lars, the clock maker's son

Read aloud pages 192 and 193.

STOP **Point to and read aloud** the first sentence on page 193.

Ask: Is this sentence telling us something or asking something? telling

Explain that sentences ending with periods are telling sentences.

Point to and read aloud the second sentence on page 193.

Ask: Is this sentence telling us something or asking something? asking What mark do you see at the end of this sentence? a question mark

3

Explain that a sentence ending with a question mark asks something. When we read a question, our voice rises at the end.

STOP **Model** how to read the second sentence on page 193 by raising your voice on the last words, *my boy.*

Read aloud pages 194 and 195.

Ask: Are there any questions on these pages or are they all sentences that tell us something? sentences that tell us something   What punctuation mark is at the end of a telling sentence? a period

Read aloud pages 196 and 197.

Ask: Can you show me somewhere on these pages that a character is speaking? Students should point to text in quotation marks.

What do we call the punctuation marks that tell us somebody is speaking? quotation marks

Can you show me somewhere on page 196 where a character is asking a question? Students should point to the question.

How do you know it is a question? It ends with a question mark.

STOP **Have students read aloud** the question at the bottom of page 196. Make sure students use correct expression and raise their voice at the end of the question.

Open and fold back the page to see **4**.

4

Read aloud pages 198–200.

Conclude by asking: Can you show me a period somewhere on the last page of the story? Students should point to one of the telling sentences.

What kind of sentence ends with a period—a telling sentence or an asking sentence? a telling sentence

When we see a period at the end of a sentence, what should we do? take a brief pause

Can you show me a question mark somewhere on the last page of the story? Students should point to one of the asking sentences.

What kind of sentence ends with a question mark—a telling sentence or an asking sentence? an asking sentence

Can you show me quotation marks somewhere on the last page of the story? Students should point to text in quotation marks.

What do quotation marks tell us? that somebody is speaking

Open and fold back the page to see **3**.

Explore "The Cap that Mother Made"
What Do You See?

Choose two of the sentences. Then, draw a picture for each sentence to show what you see in your head.

- Anders darted like an arrow down the hall.
- Anders jumped like a rabbit past the soldiers.
- Anders's face turned as red as a tomato.

Semester Review
Fiction Review

Cut out the pictures, and put them in order. Retell the story.

LITERATURE & COMPREHENSION